To Scarlett
Love forever,
Gramma
Colleen
Bean
Silly Bean.

... "prayer
changes
things +
prayer
changes
us"

My Prayer Book

My Prayer Book

Verses by Margaret Clemens
Pictures by Esther Friend

RAND McNALLY & COMPANY

NEW YORK   CHICAGO   SAN FRANCISCO

God loves us.

He wants us to talk with him.

My Prayer Book helps me
to talk with God.

My Prayer Book helps me
to say "Good morning" to God.

A New Day

Here's the sun,

Day's begun;

God be with us,

Every one.

Morning "Thank You" Prayer

I thank you, God,
For sleep last night,
I thank you for the
Morning light;
I thank you for
This happy day,
And help me keep it
Just that way.

A Morning Thought

God is near me
All the day;
He will hear me
When I pray.

My Prayer Book helps me
to talk with God.
My Prayer Book helps me
to think of God all day long.

For Little Things

For bunnies and squirrels,

For birds that have wings,

For kittens and puppies

And all little things,

Thank you, God.

Thanks for Toys

I thank you for my picture books,
I thank you for my toys;
Please help me, God, to share them
With other girls and boys.

Help Me To Remember

Today I forgot to be kind, dear God,

And friendly to everyone;

Please help me to remember,

And then we'll all have fun.

Birthday

Today is my birthday,

And I am three;

My daddy measured me

    against a tree.

There was a cake and presents,

My friends came to play.

I thank you, dear God,

For a happy, happy day.

The Wind

Dear God, the wind blew hard today,

It made me skip and run.

It tossed the clothes out on the line—

I think your wind is fun.

The Rain

I thank you, God, for rain today—
Perhaps I should explain
I have a new umbrella, and
I dearly love the rain!

Thanks for Eyes

Today I saw a little bird,
The nest is in our maple tree.
Its breast was red, its wings were blue;
Thank you, God, for eyes to see.

Thanks for Ears

Today I heard a little bird
Sing a song so sweet and clear.
"Cheerie! Cheerie!" sang the bird;
Thank you, God, for ears to hear.

My Mother and Daddy

My mother works for us each day,
And then plays with us, too.
I thank you, God, for mothers,
And everything they do.

My daddy can do anything,
He is so strong and tall.
I thank you, God, for daddies
To help us when we're small.

Thanks for Food

For fruit and milk,

For bread and meat,

For all our food so good to eat,

We thank you, God.

A Prayer at the Table

Thank you, God,
    For food so good;
And help us do
    The things we should.

A New Baby

We have a brand-new baby,

    He came home just today,

And I'm so very happy

    I don't know what to say—

    Just thank you,

    Thank you,

    Thank you, God!

Warm Clothes

I have a red sweater,
  And mittens so bright;
A snow suit with zippers,
  That covers me quite;
A scarf that wraps 'round me
  And comes to my nose;
I thank you, dear God,
  For all my warm clothes.

My Prayer Book helps me
to talk with God.
My Prayer Book helps me
to say "Good night" to God.

Day Is Done

Day is done,
    Gone the sun;
God be with us,
    Every one.

Twinkling Stars

Twinkling stars
   That shine above
Tell me, God,
   Of your dear love;
Help me know
   That you are near
A little child
   Who watches here.

Bedtime

Dear God, I've had a happy day,
I tried to do my best.
And now I thank you for the night
When children all can rest.

Evening Prayer

Dear God, hear my evening prayer:

I thank you for your love and care,

I thank you for this happy day,

For home and friends, for work and play.

Bless the ones I love tonight,

And keep us all till morning light.

E